HEY, PEANUTS!

Selected Cartoons From
MORE PEANUTS
Vol. 2

by Charles M. Schulz

A Fawcett Crest Book

Fawcett Publications, Inc., Greenwich, Conn.

Member of American Book Publishers Council, Inc.

This book, prepared especially for Fawcett Publications, Inc.,
comprises the second half ot MORE PEANUTS, and is
reprinted by arrangement witb Holt, Rinehart and Winston, Inc.

Fifteenth Fawcett Crest printing May 1968

Published by Fawcett World Library,
67 West 44th Street, New York, N. Y. 10036
Printed in the United States of America

BEDTIME!